Curious George Sees Patterns

Written by Francie Alexander

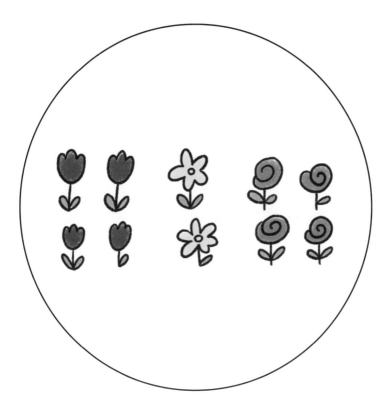

Houghton Mifflin Harcourt
Boston   New York

Patterns, patterns everywhere,
on the ground and in the air!

What patterns can you see?
Come and take a look with me.

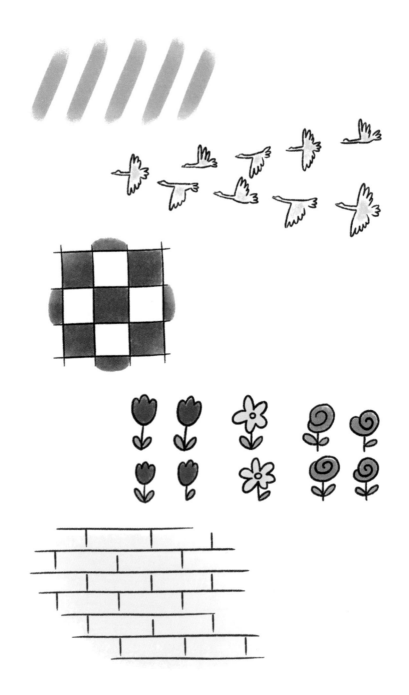

Look. There are five patterns.

The man is making a pattern
with colors.
What comes next?

Yes. Purple, orange, and red!
This will look good on George.

George is making patterns
with colors and fruits.
What comes next?

Yes. Strawberry, banana, and grape.
This looks good to eat.

Look! It's time to go.
What's next?

A party!
There are patterns all around.
How many patterns have you
found?